Enid

TIMOTHY'S
TADPOLES

Pictures by Sally Holmes and Ken Stott

COLLINS COLOUR CUBS

Timothy was rather like you – he loved kittens and puppies, little chicks and skippetty lambs. He loved visiting the farm to see the horses and cows, he loved going by the river to watch the swans sail by, and he always enjoyed going to the pond to catch the wriggling black tadpoles in the springtime.

But this year Timothy wouldn't go to the pond with the others. He didn't want to catch tadpoles.

"But why not?" said his mother. "Dick is going, and Joan. Why don't you take your net and go, too?"

"Well, Mother," said Timothy, "I've caught little black tadpoles for three years now – and our teacher at school says they turn into frogs. But they don't. They just die! And I don't want that to happen to them again this year. What's the use of my

going to the pond and fishing those funny little tadpoles out of their home, and putting them in a jam-jar, and then bringing them home to die?"

"Well, Timothy, just no use at all," said his mother, surprised. "They ought to turn into frogs, not die. There must be something wrong about the way you keep them when you bring them home."

"I wish my Uncle Fred was coming to stay," said Timothy. "He knows all about things like that. I wouldn't mind going tadpoling with him. I'm sure *his* tadpoles would grow into frogs!"

Well, Timothy got a surprise on Saturday morning – for who should turn up but his favourite Uncle Fred! He shouted to Timothy, and the little boy ran to greet him.

"Timothy! It's a marvellous day – what about going tadpoling?" said Uncle Fred.

Mother laughed when she heard that. "Tim won't go tadpoling this year," she said. "He says that he's not going to bring tadpoles home to die. He only wants them if they will live and show him how they change into little frogs."

"Quite right, too," said Uncle Fred. "I wouldn't dream of bringing home anything that was going to die. I wouldn't be so cruel. No, Timothy – we'll go and get some tadpoles that will live happily at home with you, and show you exactly how they change into frogs."

"Well, all the other children's tadpoles die, too," said Timothy. "It's horrid. Hardly any of them live to change into frogs."

"Get your net and a glass jam-jar and we'll go right away," said Uncle Fred. Mother quickly cut some sandwiches for them, and off they went.

It was a lovely walk to the pond. Uncle Fred knew all about birds and animals, flowers and trees, so he was a lovely person to go out with.

When they came to the pond they looked into the water.

"Stickle-backs – and hundreds and hundreds of tadpoles, little black wrigglers," said Timothy, excited. "And water-snails. Look at them! I can easily catch the tadpoles."

He caught dozens and put them into the jam-jar. But Uncle Fred soon shook his head.

"Here's your first mistake," he said. "Look – you've put about sixty tadpoles into one small jar, Tim. There isn't enough air in that water for more than six to breathe. You will have to empty out all of them except five or six."

"Really?" said Timothy surprised. But he did as he was told. He tipped up the jar, and almost all of the black tadpoles dripped back into the pond. Only six were left.

"Now we'll put a few water-snails in with them," said Uncle Fred.

"Why?" asked Timothy.

"Well, because the snails eat all the rubbish in the water and keep it pure and clean," said Uncle Fred. "They are the dustmen of the pond, you know. So we will put four or five into our jar."

In they went. Then Uncle Fred made Timothy pull up a little bright green water-weed for the jar.

"We'll make the jar as like a little pond as we can," he said. "Tadpoles like the water-weed in the pond – so they shall have some in their jar. There – doesn't it look nice, Timothy?"

It did. Timothy was pleased. "I'd like to take the jar home and show Mother the

tadpoles, water-weed, and all the snails," he said. "Let's have our sandwiches and then go home."

So they ate their lunch, and watched the little black moorhens that swam across the pond, bobbing their heads to and fro like clockwork.

Then they went home. Timothy carried the jar very carefully.

They met some other children, who also had jam-jars full of tadpoles.

"Is that all the tadpoles you could find, Tim?" they cried. "Look at ours! We've got hundreds."

"That's too many for your small jars," said Timothy. "Yours will die. Mine won't."

When he got home Timothy showed his mother the jar of tadpoles and snails. She thought it looked very nice. "Now go and put it in the playroom," she said. So off went Tim. He chose a very sunny window-sill and put the jar of tadpoles there, right in the golden sunshine.

Uncle Fred came in. He stared at the jar. "I say, Tim!" he said, "do you want to cook your poor tadpoles? The sun will make that water so warm that they will be almost cooked in half-an-hour's time!"

"I thought they liked the sun," said Timothy.

"So they do – but not when they are in a small jar instead of a big, cool pond where there are all sorts of places they can hide in if they get too hot," said his Uncle. "My word, Tim – no wonder your poor tadpoles die every year if you cook them in the sun."

"I think I've been rather silly before," said Timothy, going red. "I've over-crowded the poor things in a small jar – and cooked them in the sun, too. No wonder they died. Do you think they would like to be on the other window-sill, Uncle, where it's warm but not in the sun?"

"Yes," said his Uncle. So the jar of tadpoles went there.

"What do I feed them on?" asked Timothy. "I usually put bread in."

"Yes – and it goes all bad and sour in the water!" said Uncle Fred. "No – no bread, Tim."

"If you want to feed them properly it's best to go to the pond each day and bring back a tin of pond-water. There is lots of insect-life in the water that the growing tadpoles feed on. But if the pond is too far you must get a bit of raw meat from Mother, tie it to a thread, and let it hang in the water for a while. The tadpoles

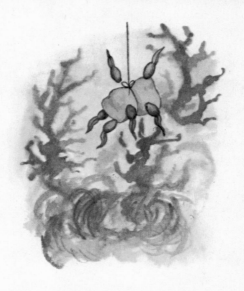

will come to feed on it, and when they have had enough you can pull the meat out by the thread. It won't go bad then, and make the water bad, too,'' said Uncle Fred.

So sometimes Timothy gave his tadpoles a tiny bit of meat tied to a thread, and sometimes he went to the pond and brought back a tin of water to add to the jar.

His tadpoles grew. How they grew! And one morning Mother heard such squeals coming from the playroom that she really had to go and see what the matter was.

"My tadpoles have got back legs! They've got back legs!" cried Timothy. "Look! Look! Soon they'll have front legs, too, and then they will really begin to look like frogs!"

Well, they got their front legs, too. Then their long tails seemed to get shorter and shorter – and before long those tadpoles began to look much more like little frogs than like black tadpoles!

"Mother," said Timothy one day, "do you know, it's very sad – *all* those tadpoles that Dick and Joan caught have died. Every single one. And all mine are alive, and have turned into tiny frogs. Today I put a bit of wood to float at the top of the jar, so that they could climb up on it and breathe the air there. Mother, soon I can let them free. They will live in our garden."

"Well, I hope they won't do any harm," said Mother.

"Uncle Fred says they will be friends to us," said Timothy. "They will eat caterpillars, grubs, and flies. Mother, won't it be fun to see little frogs working for us in our garden? Whenever I see them I shall think, 'Ha! You were once my little black tadpoles!'"

I've seen Timothy's little frogs. They are still very small, because it will take them five years to be grown-up frogs. But although they are small, what a lot of flies and grubs they eat! Ah, they are Timothy's friends all right!

And Timothy says: If *you* go to catch
tadpoles, do what he did, please. Only put
a few in a jar – keep them out of the sun –
and feed them properly. Then you, too,
will have the joy of seeing them turn into
frogs, and work for you in your garden!

ISBN 0 00 123733 0
Text © Darrell Waters Ltd
from *Tales After Tea*
Illustrations © William Collins Sons & Co Ltd 1982
Printed in Great Britain